Aerobics

Jeff Savage

Crestwood House
Parsippany, New Jersey

Designer: Deborah Fillion
Photo credits—Cover: Reebok
 Jeff Savage: pp. 4, 7, 13, 14, 18, 19, 22, 26, 29, 30, 32, 35, 37, 38, 40
 Reebok: pp. 1, 10, 21, 43
 International Association of Fitness Professionals (IDEA): p. 16

Published by Crestwood House, an imprint of Silver Burdett Press.
A Simon & Schuster Company
299 Jefferson Road, Parsippany, NJ 07054

First Edition

Printed in the United States of America

10 9 8 7 6 5 4 3 2 1

Library of Congress Cataloging-in-Publication Data
Savage, Jeff, 1961—
    Aerobics / by Jeff Savage.—1st ed.
        p. cm.—(Working Out)
    Includes index.
    ISBN 0-89686-853-2   Pbk 0-382-24945-3
    1. Aerobic exercises—Juvenile literature. 2. Physical fitness—Juvenile literature.
[1. Aerobic exercises. 2. Exercise. 3. Physical fitness.] I. Title. II. Series.
GV481.S268 1995
613.7—dc20   93-37296

A beginner's guide to aerobic exercise. Includes examples of different types of
aerobics and a glossary of terms.

CONTENTS

Regular aerobic exercise will help you maintain a healthy lifestyle.

CHAPTER 1

Discovering Aerobics

The students at Taylor School on Chicago's Southeast Side were nervous. A stranger was in their gymnasium, telling them that for the next three months they would be participating in some crazy dance program. The stranger's name was Debbie Ban-Pillarella. She explained to the 12- and 13-year-old students that the dance program would be good for them. She called the program **aerobics**.

Every weekday before school, Debbie said, she planned to arrive at the corner of 99th Street and Avenue H, walk into the school gym, and teach the students how to perform **step aerobics**. Many of the students were skeptical. After all, they already had a physical education class. Why did they need to come to school early just to jump around?

When the students showed up at the gym the following morning, they found several rows of plastic benches spread across the floor. These benches, called steps, were a yard long, a foot wide, and a few inches high. There was one step for each student.

Debbie plugged a boom box into the wall and turned on some music. It was "U Can't Touch This," by M. C. Hammer. Everyone knew the song. Debbie put her hands on her hips and swayed to the rhythm. The students watched as Debbie stepped up on her plastic bench with one foot, then the other. Then she stepped back down. Then up on the step again. Then back down. Some of the students wanted to try it. Others thought the routine was silly.

For the next hour, Debbie demonstrated some of the basic steps of aerobics—the step out, crossover, knee bends, hops, and stretch-around sways. Soon most of the students were standing up on their steps, imitating Debbie. They jumped and clapped to several songs—and found that it was fun!

As the last tune ended and Debbie led the students on a "cooldown" stretch, she observed four girls sitting on the floor in the back of the room. They had not participated in the aerobics session, and they didn't seem to want to be there at all. Debbie noticed as she walked over to the girls that all of them looked overweight.

"We just don't want to do it, that's all," one of the girls told Debbie.

"That's fine," Debbie said. "Just do me one favor. Meet me here for class tomorrow morning a few minutes early. If you still don't want to participate after tomorrow, that's fine." The girls reluctantly agreed.

The next morning, the overweight girls arrived at the gym before the rest of the students. Debbie was waiting for them.

*Debbie combines fun moves with lively music to keep her class moti-
vated.*

"Now, then," she said, "tell me why it is you don't want to participate."

Rosie spoke up. "Because," she said, "it's embarrassing to be so fat."

"Oh?" Debbie said. "Tell me about it."

"People are always making fun of us," Rosie said. "They say when we weigh ourselves, we break the scale."

The other girls confessed that they had been teased as well. Debbie listened for a while, then said, "What do you think you could do to make a change? How could you lose weight?"

"It's hopeless," Maria said. "I'm 12 years old. My mom's fat. My dad's fat. Everyone in my family is fat. I'll always be fat, too."

The girls told Debbie that they never exercised. When they weren't at school, they spent most of their time watching television. In fact, most weekends they didn't even leave the house. "What do you think of me?" Debbie asked the girls.

"Oh, you're so lucky," Brenda said. "You're so fit, and you don't have any fat, and you're pretty."

Debbie smiled. She reached behind her and pulled out a scale for the girls to see. "What do you think I weigh?" she asked.

"One hundred pounds," the girls agreed.

Debbie stood on the scale. She weighed 140 pounds, which surprised the girls. Debbie explained the difference between fat and muscle. Muscle weighs more than fat but is more compact—it takes up less space. And, of course, muscle is necessary for physical activity. She said that the most important measurement is not weight but **body fat**. Each of the girls was over 50 percent body fat, which meant that more than half her total weight was fat. For Debbie, only 15 percent of her body weight was made up of fat.

"Now, look at me. And look at you," Debbie said. "You see, it's important to get exercise, and it's important to eat healthy meals."

The girls listened, but still they were not convinced.

"I have just one more question for you," Debbie said. "I'm 33 years old. What do think I was like when I was your age?"

"Oh, you were probably on the basketball team and the softball team," Alicia said, "and you were really good-looking."

Debbie reached into her gym bag again, and pulled out an old book. It was her seventh-grade yearbook. She opened the book and pointed to a picture of a very fat girl. "Guess who this is," she said. The girls looked at the picture. They did not recognize the girl. "It's me," Debbie said. "When I was your age, I was extremely overweight. I was only 5 feet tall, but I weighed over 170 pounds."

The girls' mouths fell open. They could not believe it.

"I was teased, just like you," Debbie said. "But I decided to do something about it. I decided to make a big change in my life and become healthy. I started exercising regularly. It was hard at first, but I stuck with it. I was determined. You can do it, too. You just have to make up your mind that you don't want to be fat."

The four girls showed up for class the next day. They each set a plastic step on the floor in front of them. And when the music started, they joined the rest of the class in doing aerobics. They were on their way.

Any exercise that keeps your body in motion—from marching in place to funky street dancing—is considered an aerobic activity.

CHAPTER 2

A Breath of Fresh Air

Most of us are familiar with the basics of the human body. For instance, we know that our heart is on our left side and that we have two lungs for breathing oxygen. And we know that the farther we run, the more tired and out of breath we become. But how many of us understand why, or know what we can do to improve our fitness?

Why is it that some people can run more than 1 mile while others can't run 100 yards without stopping to rest? During gym class did you ever notice that those with the energy are the ones who are the most active? And that those who don't have much energy usually are the ones standing around or sitting down? Well, that's the basic principle of aerobics.

The level at which we are able to be physically active without getting tired is called **endurance**. The longer we can be active, the more endurance we have. The purpose of aerobics is to increase our endurance.

Let's say, for example, that in gym class you were told that in two weeks you would have to run as far as you could without stopping. Your grade would be based on how far you could run. What would you do? Would you save up all your energy by avoiding exercise? Or would you run every day and allow your body to adapt to running?

If you decided to save your energy, you would be in trouble. In order for your body to perform, you have to get it accustomed, sometimes gradually, to do what you want it to do. The key is to **train** your body. Suppose you start running 1 mile a day. After a few days, you will find it easier to run that mile—because your body is getting used to running that distance. So you might decide to run a bit farther. Then, a few days later, farther still. What you are doing is building endurance—training your body to run. That is the purpose of aerobic training. In two weeks you might be able to run 2 miles or more—and get a good grade in your gym class.

The term *aerobic* means "using oxygen" or "living in air." Aerobic exercise is any activity that requires plenty of oxygen for an extended period (at least 20 minutes). By engaging in an aerobic activity, you are placing demands on your body to handle oxygen at a higher rate than normal. What's so important about that? Because by moving air into and out of the lungs at a higher rate, you improve your **lung capacity** (the amount of oxygen your lungs can handle). Next, you improve the strength and pumping ability of your heart. This allows more blood to be pumped

throughout the body with each heart stroke. Why is this important? Because it is your blood that transports oxygen throughout
the body. The more blood flow, the more oxygen. And it is oxygen (along with food) that provides the body with energy for
growth and activity.

*With just a few weeks of aerobic training, you're sure to see an
improvement on the track.*

Believe it or not, riding a stationary bike is an aerobic activity.

CHAPTER 3

Good Healthy Fun

I n recent years health clubs have cropped up in many communities. More people across the country are exercising than ever before. And one of the most popular activities at these health clubs is aerobics.

Exercise wasn't always so popular. In the past 30 years, people have learned a great deal about their bodies. Scientific research has shown that regular exercise not only improves our physical condition but helps prevent sickness. The nation's number one health problem is heart disease. It is a national disaster. Every year more than 1 million Americans die from heart and blood vessel disease—a death rate higher than in any other country. Millions more are crippled by heart attacks.

Scientists are constantly developing new medications to help fight sickness. But in the last three decades, they have taken a closer look at how to *prevent* sickness, not just how to treat it. Aerobics is one of the best methods of disease prevention available. Aerobics has been scientifically proven to delay the onset of heart disease, as well as many other ailments.

Each year, thousands of people participate in an international aerobics convention.

The majority of this country's population still can't pass a basic fitness test. But that is changing. As a nation, we are getting healthier. People are realizing it's a lot easier to *stay* healthy than to recover from serious illness. And aerobics is a big reason for this realization.

Aerobics has become so popular that virtually every YMCA and YWCA in the country offers an aerobics class. ESPN, a major television network, has more than two hours of aerobics programming a day. Aerobics is the official exercise program of the

U.S. armed forces. Large organizations, like the International Association of Fitness Professionals (IDEA, as it is called), have been created to spread the word on aerobics. IDEA, which is based in San Diego, has an international convention every year for thousands of people interested in aerobic exercises. Video store shelves are stocked with aerobic workout tapes. Millions of books are sold every year on aerobics. You are reading an aerobics book right now, and teenagers 30 years ago were not doing that.

Aerobics has become so popular that some health clubs offer classes every hour through the entire day and evening. Each class may have room for more than 100 participants, yet people will still have to sign up hours or even days in advance to secure a spot.

The first type of aerobic exercise was known as **basic steps**. It involved the basic movements of the arms and legs that are still used today. One of the pioneers of the original aerobics was Kenneth Cooper, a doctor who showed us how important it was to exercise. "Biologically, we're in the midst of a crisis, and the statistics on cardiovascular disease show it," Dr. Cooper wrote in 1970. Several of his books, including *Aerobics* and *The New Aerobics*, were best-sellers.

New styles of aerobics have come along in recent years. **Jazzercise** aerobics was created for people who enjoy jazz music. **Cardiofunk** aerobics features rap, pop, and funk music. Step aerobics strengthens the lower body. **Aqua aerobics** is performed in a swimming pool, with the hope of reducing injuries. **High-impact** aerobics is a workout with increased intensity,

Older people enjoy chair aerobics to stay fit.

while **low-impact** aerobics features slow-paced movements, designed to increase strength and stamina without jumping. Beginners often start out with low-impact aerobics. If done correctly, low-impact exercise can provide just as good a workout as high-impact aerobics, with less strain on the muscles and back. **Chair aerobics** is a sitting-down form of exercise, primarily for elderly people who want to stay active.

More and more aerobic equipment is available these days. Athletic companies provide state-of-the-art equipment. Hundreds of styles of outfits are available in all colors, especially for women. There are hand weights and ankle weights to make workouts more vigorous. And for those who prefer working out at home, dozens of products are available, ranging from cushion mats for

Low-impact aerobics is perfect for people of all ages who want to increase their strength and endurance without stressing their muscles and joints by jumping and running.

about $20 to elaborate stair climbers for as much as $1,000.

But while aerobic styles have changed, the idea remains the same—to keep the body in motion for at least 20 minutes.

Why is this so important? Why should we keep our bodies in motion?

Life as we know it has changed a great deal in the last half century, particularly because of two inventions—the automobile and the television. People used to walk much more than they do today. Now, instead of walking a mile to school, we take the bus. Instead of walking to the grocery store, we drive the car. We are in so much of a hurry that when we go to a fast-food restaurant, we don't even leave our cars; we use the drive-through to get our meals. It seems that a lot of the time we save by driving, we spend in front of a television set. Not long ago, people spent their leisure time performing outdoor activities. Now everyone seems to be a couch potato. Our health has worsened because of it.

Slowly but surely, adults have become aware of the problem. This is why aerobics has become so popular. Until recently, young people have been left out. Overall, teens today are less physically fit than in earlier times. Scott Roberts is an exercise physiologist from New Mexico. He says, "It is ironic that, at a time when so many adults are improving their fitness habits, the children [and teens] in our society are in the worst shape in history."

What can young people do to make a change? Keep reading this book to find out.

You can spend a lot of money on the latest clothing styles or equipment, but the basic idea of aerobics remains the same—keep your body in motion and have fun!

Kids across the nation enjoy Heartlight Aerobics.

CHAPTER 4

Young People Get Involved

"Let's face it: kids won't exercise just to improve their health," says Mari Nichols, a fitness professional in San Diego. "Kids need to see that aerobics is fun." Nichols has designed a program called Heartlight Aerobics, which is used in more than 200 schools across the nation. In Heartlight, the students are the ones in charge. "The kids watch MTV and they tell us what songs to use," Nichols says. "Street dancing is really hot, and the kids show us the moves. We turn it all into aerobics." At the Del Mar Fair in southern California, hundreds of people came to watch students from more than 40 schools perform Heartlight Aerobics on stage. The show was a great success as the audience cheered the different aerobic moves the students did.

"Aerobics is a lot of fun," says Steve Wills, a 12-year-old participant at the fair. "When I first saw it, I thought it was corny. Now I like it." Some of Steve's friends at school have told him they don't want to do aerobics. "They're the ones missing out," Steve says. "I kind of feel sorry for them."

Even before they reach their teenage years, most young people begin to feel self-conscious. They become concerned about how they look and act in front of other kids their age. "It is hard to get young people to care about their own health," says Jennifer Yonekura, a physical education teacher at Bernardo Heights Middle School in Rancho Bernardo, California. "Teens are into the coolness stage. Some of them think they're too cool to jump around to music."

Well, there's nothing cool about being unhealthy. It isn't cool to be out of breath after a short run. Each year for the last decade, more than half the young people in the United States ages 6 through 17 failed the basic fitness test at their school.

But things are beginning to change. Aerobics is starting to become popular with teens. For example, in 1991 at Bernardo Heights Middle School, only 3 boys from seventh and eighth grade joined a voluntary aerobics class. A year later that number rose to 14. In 1993, 23 boys participated in the aerobic routine. Jennifer, the physical education teacher, says that after the first two minutes of laughing and looking around at who's watching them, the boys concentrate on what they're doing. "They get really fired up," she says. "And they're really sweating at the end."

A step aerobics program taught in the Midwest by Debbie Ban-Pillarella is designed to let the students be the leaders. Debbie shows the young people how to do the moves, and then they take over. The kids give each of the moves a new name. They call the step that exercises the **quadriceps,** in the upper leg, the "quadrabunga." The movement that exercises the upper arm is called the "bicep bebop." A step up and leap into the air is named the "Jordan slam dunk," after former Chicago Bulls basketball star Michael Jordan. Usually Debbie stands off to the side and lets the students take charge. Five students stand in front of the rest of the class and lead the routine. After about ten minutes, they step forward, each giving a high five to another student, and those five students run up to the front of the class to become the new leaders. Finally, after the half-hour routine and a thorough cooldown, the students sit on the floor for a talking session called "Kid Rap."

A note card with a question on it is selected by one student out of a pack of cards. The question might ask: "What is the best way to handle pressure from your boyfriend?" Or "Should you do something if you see your best friend cheating on a test?" Debbie says that the schools in the Midwest have enjoyed this program. "Kids are active in this type of class," she says. "It works a lot better than the phys ed teacher always blowing the whistle, telling them what to do."

At the downtown YMCA in San Diego, instructors Mary Gwinn and Terry Wilson lead a group of older people in a program using chair aerobics. In it, the elderly participants perform various arm and leg movements while seated in chairs. And the senior citizens love it. "If I had known when I was 12 years old what I know now, I would have done aerobics all my life," says Bill Whitaker, who is 85. "Of course, they didn't have aerobics when I was young. I sure wish they did."

Be sure to give your body a good stretch before beginning your workout.

CHAPTER 5

A Few Good Moves

There are many ways to perform aerobics. That's because there are several different styles of aerobics today. As we mentioned earlier, the first type was called basic steps. Then came step aerobics, in which a small bench is used. Other aerobic routines depend on what kind of music is used. There is jazzercise (using jazz music), cardiofunk (using rap, funk, and pop music), and several other types of routines using disco, country, rock, and old-time dance favorites like the Charleston. Speed and intensity levels range from high-impact to low-impact aerobics.

To give you an idea of how to perform aerobics, we will explain a routine from basic aerobics.

There are two important things to remember before beginning any aerobics routine. First, you must give your body a good stretch. Here's one: Stand up straight and raise your hands together high in the air to stretch your arms. Lean slowly to one side, then the other, to stretch your sides. Lean forward and try to reach for your toes to stretch your legs. If you are not in good physical shape, don't bend too close to your toes—you may strain your lower back. Do several knee bends (squat down, then come back up) with your feet shoulder width apart, to further stretch your legs. Be sure to stop the routine immediately if you get overheated or feel dizzy. Remember the four overweight girls who agreed to do aerobics after talking with Debbie? When the girls first began, all of them had to stop and rest for a moment several times during the 50-minute routine. "Alicia's face was so red and she was so overheated the first two weeks," Debbie says. "But she stuck with it, and eventually she was able to go the entire hour without stopping to rest!"

Before you begin, turn on your favorite music. Now start the basic aerobic routine. Inhale as you raise your arms up in front of you and overhead, then exhale as your arms come down to shoulder height. Do this exercise 4 times.

March in place by raising your right knee to stomach level, then stepping back down and raising your left knee the same way. As you march in place, your opposite arm (right knee, left arm) should move back and forth. Clap on the fourth count. In other words, you should step with the right knee, step with the left, step with the right, and step with the left and clap. Do this exercise 6 times (a total of 24 steps).

Now switch to **reaches**. Reach up with your right arm as high as you can, then bring your right arm back down and reach high with your left arm. Go back and forth—right arm, left arm, right arm, left arm—like climbing a ladder with your hands. Do this exer-

Warming up your muscles before a workout will increase your performance and reduce your risk of injury.

cise 8 times at normal speed, then 8 times at double speed, 8 more at normal speed, 8 more at double speed.

Run in place for 16 steps (8 for each foot), then jump using both feet with arms raised high 4 times. Do 16 more steps running, then 4 more jumps with arms high.

Now do 8 **jumping jacks**. Stand with your feet together and hands at your sides (starting position). Jump and land with your feet wide apart while clapping high over your head, then jump back to the starting position.

March 8 times, then make a quarter turn to your right and face the next wall (or to the right). Do 8 more jumping jacks. March 8 more times and make another quarter turn. Then do 8 more jumping jacks, 8 more marches, and a quarter turn. Finish with 8 more

You can add several types of arm movements while jogging in place to create an interesting aerobic routine.

jumping jacks, 8 more marches, and another quarter turn. You should now be back where you began, facing in the original direction.

Next is the **hand jive**. Touch your right hand to your left shoulder, then touch your left hand to your right shoulder. Next, place your right hand on your right hip, then place your left hand on your left hip. Now extend your right arm forward with palm facing up, then extend your left arm forward with palm facing up. Next, turn your right palm face down, then your left palm face down. Finish the hand jive by placing your hands on your hips and bending your knees, then stepping forward on your left heel, then your right heel, then your left, then your right, back and forth 8 times for each heel.

Finish up by doing 8 jumping jacks and 8 marches followed by a quarter turn. Do this routine four times until you've returned to your original position.

This basic routine should last about five minutes. If you can do the routine at least four times (20 minutes or more), then you are performing aerobics the correct way. You can, of course, change the routine by doing the movements in any order you wish, as long as you do them well. The higher you step and the higher you reach, the better. What's more, you can create new routines with your friends. Just remember to have fun.

Riding a skateboard is a good way to get aerobic exercise and social-
ize with your friends.

CHAPTER 6

Aerobic Alternatives

Remember the purpose of aerobics? It's to get your heart pumping, your blood flowing, and most important, it's for you to breathe as much oxygen as you can. Aerobics as you've learned it–marching in place, reaches, hand jives, and the other moves–is one of the best ways to accomplish this. But it's not the *only* way. There are dozens of sports and activities that can give you a good aerobic workout.

It's simple: An activity is aerobic when it keeps you moving for at least 20 minutes. An activity is **anaerobic** when it does not involve continuous movement. Weight lifting is an example of an anaerobic workout. It involves a few moments of energy when you are lifting the weights, followed by a few moments of rest. If you are starting and stopping like that, you are not getting an aerobic workout.

Would you say running is aerobic or anaerobic? Well, it depends on the type of running. Running long, slow distances, like the marathon, is aerobic. But running with short bursts of speed, like the 100-meter dash, is anaerobic. A man interested in aerobics wrote to Kenneth Cooper, the doctor who helped develop aerobics, with this question: "I timed myself for a quarter mile. Sixty-three seconds! How does this rate for fitness?" Dr. Cooper's answer was: "It doesn't. You're fast all right. But dash speed (anaerobics) is unrelated to basic fitness. What counts is endurance (aerobics), which is a direct measure of heart-lung capacity."

So, running *can* be aerobic, if it involves long, slow distances, like jogging. Here are several other sports and activities that can be aerobic:

Swimming. This is a terrific aerobic exercise, especially if you're swimming in the deep end of the pool, or in a lake or the ocean, and you can't touch the bottom with your feet. Even treading water will give you a great workout. Water polo is a good aerobic activity, too, and so is surfing. Have you ever seen an overweight surfer?

Cycling. This is another great aerobic activity, and it helps improve your leg strength as well. It's important to ride the bike for at least half an hour. Just peddling around the corner doesn't count, and neither does coasting downhill. People who don't own a bicycle can ride exercise bikes (stationary bikes) at their local health club. It provides the same aerobic workout.

Hiking. This is a great way to get exercise, and it can be an adventure, too. Find the nearest trail, hill, or mountain and go. Just try not to get lost.

Surfing can keep you fit and *cool in warm weather.*

Basketball. Of the four most popular professional sports (baseball, football, basketball, hockey) in this country, this one is the best aerobically. Basketball is most effective if you are playing full court (not half court), if you are hustling, if you aren't stopping all the time for free throws, and if you aren't calling time-outs. (By the way, hockey is the second best aerobically.)

Soccer. This is the most popular sport in the world, but it hasn't been that popular in the United States—at least, not professionally. Many communities have soccer clubs for kids and teens. If you can join a team, do it.

A few other activities include tennis (with long rallies), skateboarding, roller-skating, martial arts, dancing (fast), and skiing. Can you think of any others?

Believe it or not, even walking is a form of aerobics! At the Pacific Beach Recreation Center in San Diego, teenagers participate in a walking program each day after school. Participants either walk a designated course at the recreation center or take the walking tour up winding roads to a hilltop known as Mt. Soledad. They are rewarded for the time they walk relative to their age. Participants who walk as many minutes as their age receive a star. For instance, if a 14-year-old girl walks 28 minutes, she gets two stars. The stars are placed next to the participants' names, which are posted on boards hanging in the recreation center. Prizes are awarded each month for those who earn the most stars.

"It's a good contest," says Deron Simon, the recreation center manager who created the program. "Boys generally are more com-

This girl is getting a terrific aerobic workout while enjoying one of the most popular sports in the country.

Jumping jacks—an easy aerobic exercise and a perfect way to warm up before a big game.

petitive than girls, but we have a large percentage of girls who participate, especially teens."

Simon, who leads most of the walking tours to Mt. Soledad, says that sometimes as many as 30 walkers will go with him. "Some of the younger kids think it's a race, and as soon as we get within eyesight of the top, they'll sprint the rest of the way. The teenagers are too cool to run."

Simon says boys are enthusiastic about the program until about age 12, when they become more interested in basketball and other sports. That is not the case with girls. "I don't know if the teenage girls are in it for the enjoyment of walking or the competition," he says, "but they sure do accumulate a lot of stars."

A daily outdoor walk will do wonders for your health and appearance.

CHAPTER 7

Just Do It

Making a big change is hard to do, especially for young people. There are so many other things to worry about, so many people to please. They have to please their parents, their teachers, their friends, their classmates, their neighbors, and on and on. But for you, when it comes to taking care of your body, it is *your* responsibility. You have to please yourself. Remember: If you feel great and look great, you are the one who is winning.

There are so many reasons to get involved in aerobics.

A fitness expert named Karen Clippinger-Robertson said in a speech a few years ago that there is a "critical period" around puberty when the body can make great gains in physical fitness. Teens who exercise aerobically during the period between 11 and 14 years of age will probably feel better and look better for the rest of their lives. Do you want to miss out on this "critical period"? Of course, nobody should stop working out after age 14! And if you're older than 14 now, it's not too late to start an exercise routine. But no matter how old you are, it's a good idea to have a complete physical exam before you begin working out.

For students who have a hard time concentrating in school

(especially on tests), doing aerobics on a regular basis can help. Scott Roberts (the exercise physiologist from New Mexico) says, "It does appear that healthy bodies make healthy minds."

For teens who are concerned about what their friends and classmates think of them, aerobics is a great way to look better.

For those who want to have fun with others, aerobics is a terrific way to socialize.

Laura Bottero, an exercise specialist in New York City, says, "Adults already have discovered the joy of aerobics. It's about time kids find out, too."

When you begin your aerobic routine, remember that you won't change overnight, or even in a week. It's going to take some time and dedication. In Kathy Smith's *Winning Workout* videotape, Smith says, "Set a schedule and stick to it. You're going to see results soon enough." The four overweight girls in the first chapter didn't see any changes in their bodies for the first few weeks. But they stuck to it. And eventually the workout paid off. Alicia lost 35 pounds in one year. Rosie lost 30 pounds and now eats more vegetables and less junk food. Brenda and Maria each lost more than 20 pounds. "All the girls look better," says Debbie Ban-Pillarella, "and they feel better about themselves. They're happier now."

It doesn't matter whether you choose high- or low-impact aerobics, step aerobics, or any other aerobic sport or activity you can think of. What matters is that you choose something and stick to it. Just do it.

* * *

Millions of teens are looking and feeling better because they've discovered the joy of aerobics. Join them!

To Find Out More About Aerobics

BOOKS

Cooper, Dr. Kenneth H. *Aerobics Program*. 1985. Bantam Books.

Haas, Dr. Robert. *Eat to Win: The Sports Nutrition Bible*. 1985. NAL-Dutton.

Liptak, Karen. *Aerobics Basics*. 1983. Prentice-Hall.

Rosas, Debbie and Carlos. *Non-impact Aerobics*. 1988. Avon.

VIDEOS

Aerobikids. Orthopedic Physical Therapy Products, 3750 Annapolis Lane, Minneapolis, MN 55441.

Kathy Smith's Winning Workout. Media Home Entertainment, Inc., 75 Rockefeller Plaza, New York, NY 10019.

Teen Workout. Tamilee Webb, Field Communications, 245 Long Hill Road, Middletown, CT 06457.

WHERE TO WRITE FOR INFORMATION

American Alliance for Health, Physical Education, Recreation
and Dance (AAHPERD)
1900 Association Drive
Reston, VA 22091

American Heart Association
1615 Stemmons Freeway
Dallas, TX 75207

IDEA: The International Association of Fitness Professionals
6190 Cornerstone Court East, Suite 204
San Diego, CA 92121-3773

President's Council on Physical Fitness and Sports
Suite 250, 701 Pennsylvania Avenue NW
Washington, DC 20004

Glossary

aerobics Any activity that requires continuous use of oxygen.

anaerobic activity Any activity that does not require the continuous use of oxygen.

aqua aerobics Aerobic exercise performed in a swimming pool.

basic step The original form of aerobics, performed standing on the floor.

body fat The amount of fat as a percentage of total body weight.

cardiofunk A more recent form of aerobic exercise in which rap, pop, or funk music is used.

chair aerobics Aerobic exercise performed while in a seated position.

endurance The degree to which a person can go without running out of energy.

hand jive An aerobic exercise technique that features hand movements to the shoulder, hip, and so on.

high-impact A level of aerobic exercise in which the participants move at a rapid pace.

jazzercise A style of aerobic exercise in which jazz music is used.

jumping jacks A traditional exercise technique in which the exerciser jumps and lands with feet apart while clapping overhead.

low-impact A level of aerobic exercise in which the participants move at a slow but steady pace.

lung capacity The amount of oxygen a person can process through his or her body.

quadriceps The large muscle at the front of the thigh.

reaches An aerobic exercise technique in which one arm, then the other, is raised high.

step aerobics Aerobic exercises performed by stepping on and off a plastic bench. Step aerobics are designed to strengthen the lower body.

train To improve fitness by pushing the body to handle more exercise.

Index